Developing Num

USING AND APPLYING MATHS

INVESTIGATIONS FOR THE DAILY MATHS LESSON

year

R

Hilary Koll and Steve Mills

A & C BLACK

C000001778

Mathematical skills and processes

Page	Activity title	Predict	Visualise	Look for pattern	Record	Reason	Make decisions	Estimate	Explain	Be systematic	Co-operate	Compare	Test ideas	Trial and improvement	Ask own questions
	Counting and recognising numbers														
12	Pick a pair				●	○					○				
13	Snowman buttons	●				○						○	●		
14	Animal hospital	○			●										
15	How many legs?				●		●								
16	All about 3			●		●			○						
17	Furniture fun				●		●			○					
18	Toy maze			●	○		○		○			○			
19	Fish bowls	●	●					○				○			
20	Duck ponds	●	●					○				○			
21	Letter count			○					○			●	●		
22	Jigsaw			○	○	○				●			○	●	
23	In the garden		●			○			○			○			
24	Asking game										●	○			●
	Adding and subtracting														
25	Jack's magic beans				●		○		○			○			
26	Spacehoppers	○		●	●					●		○			○
27	Busy bees			●		○						○			
28	Kitten on the stairs	○		●	○				○	●		○			
29	The dinner queue			●		○						○			
30–31	At the café: 1 and 2				●		●								○
32	Peas in a pod				●	○	○			●					
33	Marbles	●	○									○	○		
34	Biscuit take away	○		●	○	○			○			○	○		
35	Crazy caterpillars			●		○			○		●				
	Measures, shape and space														
36	Swirling spirals	●				○					○		●		
37	Roll and slide	●	●		○						○		●		○
38	Paperclip pythons	●											●		
39	Who can see who?		●			○									
40	Teddy boys								○		●	○	○	○	
41–43	Stepping out	○	○		●		●					○			
44	Smiley faces	●	●										●		
45	Jamie's jumper	○		●									○		
46	Sorting signs				●				●			○			
47	Lunch boxes	○	●	○	●						○			○	
48	A classroom hunt				●	○	●					○	○		

● Key processes identified on the activity sheet   ○ Additional processes involved in the activity

Contents

Counting and recognising numbers

Adding and subtracting

3

Measures, shape and space

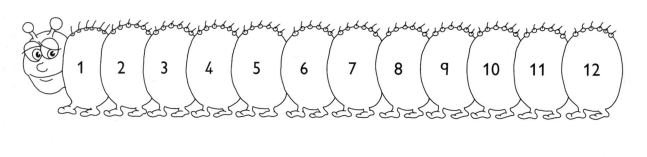

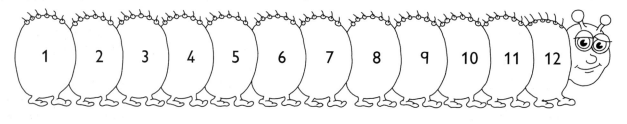

Published 2005 by A & C Black Publishers Limited
37 Soho Square, London W1D 3QZ
www.acblack.com

ISBN-10: 0-7136-7135-1
ISBN-13: 978-0-7136-7135-3

Copyright text © Hilary Koll and Steve Mills, 2005
Copyright illustrations © Sarah Wimperis, 2005
Copyright cover illustration © Charlotte Hard, 2005
Editors: Lynne Williamson and Marie Lister
Designer: Heather Billin

The authors and publishers would like to thank Jane McNeill and Catherine Yemm for their advice in producing this series of books.

A CIP catalogue record for this book is available from the British Library.

All rights reserved. This book may be photocopied, for use in the school or educational establishment for which it was purchased, but may not be reproduced in any other form or by any means – graphic, electronic or mechanical, including recording, taping or information retrieval systems – without the prior permission in writing of the publishers.

Printed in Great Britain by Cromwell Press, Trowbridge, Wiltshire.

A & C Black uses paper produced with elemental chlorine-free pulp, harvested from managed sustainable forests.

Introduction

Developing Numeracy: Using and Applying Maths is a series of seven photocopiable activity books designed to be used during the daily maths lesson. The books focus on using and applying mathematics, as referred to in the National Numeracy Strategy *Framework for teaching mathematics*. The activities are intended to be used in the time allocated to pupil activities during the main part of the lesson. They are designed to develop and reinforce the skills and processes that are vital to help children use and apply their maths.

Using and applying mathematics

There are several different components which make up the **content** of maths and form the bulk of any maths curriculum:

- **mathematical facts**, for example, a triangle has three sides;
- **mathematical skills**, such as counting;
- **mathematical concepts**, like place value.

For maths teaching to be successful, it is vital that children can *use* this mathematical content beyond their classroom, either in real-life situations or as a basis for further understanding. However, in order to do so, they require extra abilities over and above the mathematical content they have learned. These extra abilities are often referred to as the **processes** of mathematical activity. It is these processes which make mathematical content usable.

As an example, consider this question:
How many triangles are there in this shape?

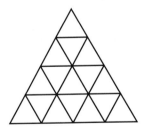

The mathematical content required is only:
- the **fact** that a triangle has three sides;
- the **skill** of counting.

As such, it could be expected that very young children could solve this problem. The fact that they cannot suggests that other abilities are involved. These are the processes, and for this question they include:
- visualising the different-sized triangles;
- being systematic in counting all the triangles of different sizes;
- looking for patterns in the numbers of triangles;
- trial and improvement;
- recording.

Unless children can apply these processes in this situation, then however good their counting skills and knowledge of triangles may be, they will fail.

The 'solving problems' strand of the *Framework for teaching mathematics* emphasises the importance of using and applying mathematics. This series of books is intended to make explicit the skills and processes involved in learning how to put maths knowledge to use.

Using and Applying Maths Year R supports the development of the using and applying processes by providing opportunities to introduce and practise them through a series of activities. On the whole these activities are designed for children to work on independently, although due to the young age of the children the teacher may need to read the instructions with the children and ensure that they understand the activity before they begin working on it.

Pre-school children are naturally inquisitive about the world around them. They love to explore and experiment, and to make marks and record things on paper in their own idiosyncratic ways. Unfortunately, once at school the focus is often placed firmly on the maths content alone and children can be led to believe that maths is not a subject of exploration, but rather one of simply learning the 'right way to do things'. As a result, when older children are asked to explore and investigate maths they are often at a loss if their maths teaching to date has not encouraged and built upon their natural instincts.

Year R helps children to develop the following processes:

- predicting
- visualising
- looking for pattern
- recording
- reasoning
- making decisions
- estimating
- explaining
- being systematic
- co-operating
- comparing
- testing ideas
- trial and improvement
- asking own questions

When using these activities, the focus need not be on the actual mathematical content. Instead, the teacher's demonstrations, discussions and questioning should emphasise the processes the children are using. A summary of the skills and processes covered by each activity is shown on page 2. When appropriate, invite the children to explain their thinking to others. Research has shown that children develop processes most successfully when the teacher encourages them to act as experts rather than novices, allowing them to work autonomously and encouraging a range of approaches to any problem rather than constraining discussion to produce an overall class plan. The children should evaluate their own plans against other plans in the posing, planning and monitoring phases of the lessons.

Extension

Many of the activity sheets end with a challenge (**Now try this!**) which reinforces and extends children's learning, and provides the teacher with an opportunity for assessment. Again, it may be necessary to read the instructions with the children before they begin the activity. For some of the challenges the children will need to record their answers on a separate piece of paper.

Organisation

Very little equipment is needed, but it will be useful to have available: coloured pencils, counters, dice, scissors, coins, number lines and number tracks.

To help teachers select appropriate learning experiences for the children, the activities are grouped into sections within the book. However, the activities are not expected to be used in this order unless stated otherwise. The sheets are intended to support, rather than direct, the teacher's planning.

Some activities can be made easier or more challenging by masking or substituting numbers. You may wish to re-use pages by copying them onto card and laminating them. If you find that the answer boxes are too small for the children's writing, you could enlarge the activity sheet onto A3 paper.

Teachers' notes

Brief notes are provided at the foot of each page giving ideas and suggestions for maximising the effectiveness of the activity sheets. These can be masked before copying.

Solutions and further explanations of the activities can be found on pages 7–11, together with examples of questions that you can ask.

Whole class warm-up activities

The following activities provide some practical ideas which can be used to introduce the main teaching part of the lesson.

Number snakes

This activity focuses on predicting where a particular number is in a sequence. Draw a number snake on the board and fill in several numbers, counting on either in ones or in twos, for example:

Ask the class: *Where do you think the number 7 will be?*

An alternative idea is to ask the children to predict which number will be in the head of the snake, like this:

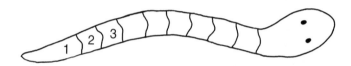

How many cubes?

Hold some cubes in your hand and show them to the children. Ask: *How many cubes do you think I have in my hand?* Discuss estimates and then count to check. Invite several children to take a handful of cubes themselves and ask them to predict who has the most. Again, ask for estimates and then count to check.

Picture a shape

For practice in visualising, hide a flat shape in a cloth bag. Put your hand into the bag and describe the shape to the children: for example, *Ouch! Ouch! Ouch! This shape has three corners. It has three straight sides. What do you think it looks like?*

Shapes and colours

Use this activity to introduce the idea of working systematically. Draw a square, circle and triangle on the board and discuss their shape names. Explain that you can have red, blue or yellow shapes and ask the children to suggest what you could draw: for example, a red circle, a yellow triangle, a blue square. Using their suggestions, draw each of the nine possibilities on the board, asking questions like: *How many yellow shapes have we drawn? How many triangles have we drawn? Are we missing any?* (Logiblocs could be used for this activity.) Extend the activity by introducing another colour, such as green.

Notes on the activities

Counting and recognising numbers

Pick a pair (page 12)
☆ *Processes: look for pattern, reason, co-operate*
This activity encourages the children to think about which objects in real life usually come in pairs. The children can draw objects that come in pairs and make a class display of 'things that come in twos'.

Suggested questions:
- Can we count in twos the things you have drawn?
- What other things can you think of that come in twos?

Snowman buttons (page 13)
☆ *Processes: predict, test ideas, compare, record*
To give the children experience of how long one minute is, explore how much can be achieved in one minute (for example, how many bricks can be put together). After completing the activity sheet, encourage the children to compare their result with their prediction. As a further extension, ask them to record on plain paper how others did. Invite children to explain how they have shown this information.

Suggested questions:
- How many snowmen do you think you will finish?
- How many did you finish?
- What was the highest number of snowmen finished?
- How could we show everyone's results on paper?

Animal hospital (page 14)
☆ *Processes: record, predict*
This activity will help the children begin to understand the reasons for setting information out clearly, whether they use drawings, words, tallies or numbers. Decide how many animals you wish the children to record, and draw the appropriate number of horizontal lines on the chart before photocopying. Begin the lesson by telling a story along the following lines:

Miss Vernon is a vet. Each day she decides how many pills each animal should have and what time they should have them. She begins with the dog. At one o'clock the dog needs one pill. Next she looks at the rabbit. At two o'clock the rabbit needs two pills. Next she goes to the cat. At three o'clock the cat needs three pills. (Continue with other animals, encouraging the children to predict how many pills the next animal should have and at what time.)

Explain that Miss Vernon needs a chart to help her remember. Encourage the children to make their own decisions about how to record the information on the chart.

Suggested questions/prompts:
- [Claire] has drawn the pills but [Sam] has written the number. These are both clear ways of showing the information.
- Tell us about your chart.
- How did you show the time? Did you draw a clock?

How many legs? (page 15)
☆ *Processes: record, make decisions*
Allow the children to decide for themselves how best to record the number of legs each creature has. Spend time asking the children to show their recordings to the class, and discuss whose recordings are easiest to understand. The children could be shown a table of the information with two columns, headed 'Creature' and 'Number of legs'. Discuss how this can make it very easy for others to understand. The data could be arranged in order, with those with most or fewest legs first.

Suggested questions:
- Can you explain why you set it out like that?
- Do you think this is easy to understand?
- If you were to do this again, how would you set it out?

All about 3 (page 16)
☆ *Processes: look for pattern, reason, explain*
The focus of this activity is on looking for pattern, reasoning, and explaining or justifying one's ideas. There are no right or wrong answers, only children's opinions, which they should be able to explain to others and justify. Encourage the children to notice that others have different views and will see the pictures in different ways: for example, the bike sign may be viewed by one child as a triangle sign with three sides, reminding them of the number 3, whereas another child may think of the two wheels on a bike and thus not be reminded of three.

Suggested questions:
- Why did this remind you of the number 3?
- Did anyone else draw a ring around this picture?
- Can you see why this reminded [Rafiq] of the number 3 now?

Furniture fun (page 17)
☆ *Processes: record, make decisions, explain, compare*
The focus of this activity should be on allowing children to develop their own ways of recording. Each child will have a different view on how to show this information on paper. Value all types of recording and discuss the different methods used.

Suggested questions:
- Can you explain what you have drawn?
- How did you show the number of chairs we have?
- Can you tell us how many there were by looking at your paper?
- Can you see how [Jake]'s and [Li]'s ways of showing the furniture are different?
- Which way do you think was quicker?
- Which tells you the most about the furniture?

Toy maze (page 18)

☆ *Processes: look for pattern, test ideas, compare, explain, record, reason*

Emphasise that you want the children to look for patterns in the toys in the maze. These could include:
- car, ball, car, ball, car, ball
- teddy, car, ball, teddy, car, ball, teddy
- teddy, teddy, ball, teddy, teddy, ball
- car, ball, ball, car, ball, ball

You could draw on routes before photocopying for children to explain and describe.

Suggested questions/prompts:
- What is special about the toys on this path?
- Do they have a pattern?
- Explain to your partner what you notice.
- Try making a maze of your own like this.

Fish bowls (page 19)

☆ *Processes: visualise, predict, estimate, test ideas*

This activity provides practice in the important skill of visualising sets of numbers in smaller groups, rather than counting items individually. After the children have completed the activity and compared their predictions with the actual numbers of fish, discuss ways of seeing objects in groups of two or three.

Suggested questions:
- What did you see in your mind when you tried to guess which bowls had five/six fish in them?
- How good were your predictions?
- Could you count the fish by grouping in twos or threes?

Duck ponds (page 20)

☆ *Processes: visualise, predict, estimate, test ideas*

Like the previous activity, this provides practice in the important skill of visualising sets of numbers in smaller groups, rather than counting items individually.

Suggested questions:
- What did you see in your mind when you tried to guess which ponds had seven/eight ducks on them?
- How good were your predictions?
- Could you count the ducks by grouping in threes or fours?

Letter count (page 21)

☆ *Processes: test ideas, compare, explain, record, reason, look for pattern*

At the start of the lesson, encourage discussion about who in the class has a long first name and who has a short first name. When the children count the letters in the names, emphasise the importance of checking: for example, by counting backwards from the last letter to the first, or by counting letters in twos.

Suggested questions:
- How many letters do you think there are in [Christopher]'s name? Shall we count them?
- Is [Claire]'s name longer or shorter than [Sean]'s?
- Which do you think is the most common number of letters in a name?

Jigsaw (page 22)

☆ *Processes: be systematic, trial and improvement, look for pattern, record, reason, make decisions, test ideas*

The focus of this activity is on using trial and improvement strategies and developing perseverance. Many different arrangements of the jigsaw pieces can be made, but in order to make touching sides match and to succeed in using all the pieces, the children may have to try certain pieces and remove and replace them.

Suggested questions/prompts:
- Can you fit this piece into your jigsaw?
- Do these two touching sides match?
- Try moving one of your pieces.
- Have you checked all the touching sides?
- How could you make a record of your solution?

In the garden (page 23)

☆ *Processes: visualise, compare, reason, explain*

Ensure that the numbers 0 to 9 are displayed in the classroom. A similar activity can be performed practically with large plastic numerals, using a piece of paper or hand to mask parts of the numerals. When the children have written their answers, encourage them to explain their reasoning: for example, 'These parts are curved, so it must be one of the curved numbers, like 3 or 8.'

Suggested questions:
- Which number do you think this is?
- What makes you think it must be a 3?
- Do any numbers have only straight sides?
- Which numbers are curved?

Asking game (page 24)

☆ *Processes: co-operate, ask own questions, test ideas, compare*

This activity encourages co-operation and provides opportunities for children to pose and answer their own questions. At the start of the lesson, discuss suitable questions that could be asked.

Suggested questions:
- How many more/less than [six]?
- How many altogether?
- Does anyone have exactly [seven]?
- What other questions could you ask?

Adding and subtracting

Jack's magic beans (page 25)

☆ *Processes: record, explain, compare, make decisions*

The focus of this activity is on helping children to realise the importance of recording their thinking clearly. Stress that the clearer the recording, the easier it is to remember what you did and the easier it is for someone else to see your thinking. Once the children have recorded their activities several times, ask them to explain their work to a partner. The different ways of recording should be compared as a class and attention can then be drawn to any use of standard symbols, for example '='.

Suggested questions:
- Can you explain to us what this means?
- Did you draw the beans? Did anyone use a quicker way of showing the beans (such as lines or dots)?
- Do you know what this sign that [Ian] has used means?

Spacehoppers (page 26)
☆ *Processes: look for pattern, be systematic, record, predict, compare, explain, ask own questions*

Encourage the children to take this investigation further: for example, by choosing a number of hops between 1 and 9 and exploring different ways of hopping on that number. These can be recorded and displayed as wall charts or posters and can be a useful contribution to early addition and subtraction work.

Suggested questions:
- What patterns did you notice in the numbers?
- Did you work through in order, starting with 1?
- What other questions could you ask?

Busy bees (page 27)
☆ *Processes: look for pattern, reason, explain, compare*

This activity encourages children to notice that if we add two numbers together, the answer is the same regardless of the order in which we add them (for example, 4 + 1 has the same answer as 1 + 4). The children can investigate to see if this true for all pairs of numbers.

Suggested questions:
- What do you notice?
- How could this help us with other questions?
- Can you think of other pairs of questions with the same answer?

Kitten on the stairs (page 28)
☆ *Processes: look for pattern, be systematic, record, predict, compare, explain*

Invite the children to explain the patterns they notice and to suggest why they think the patterns occur. This activity can lead to exploring other patterns through jumping up or down a certain number of steps. Further extension questions could be asked about odd or even numbers, for example: 'If Jack stands on an even number and jumps down two, will he land on an even number?'

Suggested questions:
- What patterns did you notice in the numbers?
- Did you work down in order all the way to 2?
- Why do you think you stopped at 2?

The dinner queue (page 29)
☆ *Processes: look for pattern, explain, compare, reason, ask own questions*

For this activity the children will need to know ordinal numbers and be able to add two small numbers. They should be encouraged to describe what they notice when they have added the pairs of numbers, i.e. that all pairs have a total of 7. Encourage them to explain any reasons for this and to notice the link between the number 7 and the number in the queue.

Suggested questions:
- What do you notice?
- Is this the same for every pair of numbers?
- What could we do next?
- What do you think the total might be?

At the café: 1 and 2 (pages 30–31)
☆ *Processes: make decisions, record, explain, ask own questions*

Encourage discussion about the different costs of the dishes and the total cost of a main dish and dessert. Invite the children to pose their own questions. Further extension activities could include asking the children to find all the possible meals that could be bought for £6. This can help to develop the process of being systematic.

Suggested questions:
- Which main dish would you like?
- What about dessert?
- Can you think of questions to ask about the prices?
- What if the price of each dish went up by £1?

Peas in a pod (page 32)
☆ *Processes: look for pattern, be systematic, record, reason, explain*

Encourage the children to describe any patterns they notice, suggesting reasons for the patterns if they can. Draw pea pods on the board to show how the pairs of pea pods making 5 can be arranged systematically, starting with 1, then 2, and so on (i.e. 1 and 4, 2 and 3, 3 and 2, 4 and 1).

Suggested questions:
- What if you had one pea in this pod?
- What if you had two peas in this pod?
- Can you work through in an order?
- What other ways can you find?

Marbles (page 33)
☆ *Processes: predict, test ideas, visualise, compare*

Encourage the children to explain what they did when predicting which questions would have an answer greater than 6, and to compare their predictions with those of a partner. Discourage any form of counting until all predictions have been made. When the children test their predictions, remind them to use appropriate strategies such as counting on from the larger number.

Suggested questions:
- Which trays did you guess would have more than 6?
- Why did you think that this one would have a number more than 6?
- [Meena] ticked a tray and then found that it had exactly 6 marbles. Was her guess correct? Is 6 more than 6?

Biscuit take away (page 34)
☆ *Processes: look for pattern, reason, record, predict, compare, explain, be systematic*

This activity focuses on the importance of looking for patterns in subtractions and using the patterns to predict answers to other questions.

- What pattern did you notice in your answers?
- What pattern did you notice in the questions? How many biscuits are on the first plate, the second plate, the third plate…?
- Which question would come next in the pattern?
- What other questions could we answer in this way?

Crazy caterpillars (page 35)

☆ *Processes: look for pattern, co-operate, record, reason, explain*

At the start of the lesson, discuss what doubling means and demonstrate different strategies for doubling a number: for example, counting the number twice or counting in twos as you point to each dot on the dice. Encourage the children to notice that only the even numbers can be coloured, and to explain to a partner why this is the case.

Suggested questions:

- Which numbers have you coloured?
- What do you notice?

Measures, shape and space

Swirling spirals (page 36)

☆ *Processes: predict, test ideas, reason, explain, ask own questions*

This activity encourages the children to make predictions and to test their ideas practically. Some children may find the cutting out difficult, but all can make predictions and explain their reasoning. Invite them to talk about which features of the shapes helped them to make their predictions: for example, 'I think a circle will make the longest spiral,' or, 'The dotted lines are close together so it will make a long one.' Once the children have tested their ideas by making the spirals, they can then begin to revise their ideas and predict the outcomes of other shapes. Ask them to choose their own paper shape, such as a rectangle, a circle or a square, and to see whether a particular shape is better for making longer spirals. They might also notice that where cuts are made close together, a longer (and more fragile!) spiral is produced.

Suggested questions:

- Why do you think this will make the longest spiral?
- What do you think it is about the rectangle that makes it the longest spiral?
- Do you think all rectangles will make the longest spirals? How could you find out?

Roll and slide (page 37)

☆ *Processes: predict, visualise, test ideas, co-operate, record*

The children can be encouraged to record their predictions in a number of ways. Each pair could have three sheets of paper, labelled 'roll', 'slide' and 'roll and slide', and cut out the pictures and stick them onto the appropriate sheets. Alternatively, they could write 'R', 'S' or 'R S' on the sheet itself. You will need the following items (or similar) for the children to test their predictions: wooden egg, book, crayon, ball, milk carton, beaker, coin, orange, cotton reel, banana, triangle and a bowl. Discuss predictions that they did not get right (for example, the bowl may look curved but will slide rather than roll). A class poster could be created and the children could be encouraged to look for items around the school and at home to add to each section.

Suggested questions:

- Do you think the cotton reel will roll? Will it slide? Could it both roll and slide?
- What other things can you think of that roll/slide/roll and slide?
- Were you right in your predictions?

Paperclip pythons (page 38)

☆ *Processes: predict, test ideas*

Whilst this is an activity about length, the focus should also be on predicting skills. Encourage discussion about what is a good estimate and give the children an opportunity to change their estimates after the class discussion.

Then provide paperclips and ask the children to test their predictions. Rather than emphasising how accurate the estimates were, encourage the children to see how useful testing is, as it will help them to become much better at estimating next time. This could lead on to children drawing their own snakes on sheets for others to estimate and test.

Suggested questions:

- Why did you guess [eight] paperclips for this snake and only [three] for this one?
- Would anyone like to change any of their guesses?
- Did anyone have any good ideas about how to test the guesses quickly?
- Can you draw a snake that is about eight paperclips long now?
- Are you getting better at guessing?

Who can see who? (page 39)

☆ *Processes: visualise, reason, explain*

This activity gives the children an opportunity to visualise things from another's perspective. It can help to reinforce positional words such as 'between', 'next to', 'opposite'.

Suggested questions:

- Is there a wall between the spider and the mouse?
- Who can the ladybird see?
- How many creatures can the mouse see?
- I want to draw a beetle on this map so that it can see the frog and the caterpillar. Where could I draw it?

Teddy boys (page 40)

☆ *Processes: be systematic, co-operate, make decisions, compare, trial and improvement*

This activity encourages the children to begin the process of working systematically. Once the children have completed the sheet, a game can be played as a class, in which the teacher calls out descriptions such as, 'red hat, blue T-shirt, yellow shorts', and the children have to find that bear. By sorting their bears and playing the game suggested, the children are encouraged to compare the bear outfits and to begin looking for missing outfits.

Suggested questions:
- How many bears have you coloured with yellow hats?
- Can you think of another way that you could colour the outfit using red and green?
- Are any of the bears you have coloured the same?
- How did you decide what to colour next?
- Can you find a bear with blue shorts and a red T-shirt that you have coloured? What colour is the bear's hat?

Stepping out (pages 41–43)
☆ *Processes: estimate, record, predict, test ideas, visualise*

Before beginning this activity, ask the children to estimate the number of 'pigeon steps' of their own it would take to cross the classroom (placing one foot in front of the other, heel to toe). Then ask them to test their estimates. Show them the size of a 'chicken step' card (from page 42) and ask them to estimate the number of steps a chicken would take to cross a table, or to walk the length of a ruler. Then do the same with the 'duck step' cards from page 43. The children should record their estimates for different items in the classroom on the activity sheet. Give the children sets of the cards (or ask them to cut out their own), so that they can arrange the steps in a line to check their estimates.

Suggested questions:
- How many chicken steps do you think will be needed to cross the table?
- Do you think more chicken steps or duck steps will be needed to cross the table?
- How did you show your estimate on paper?
- Was your guess close to the actual number of steps?

Smiley faces (page 44)
☆ *Processes: visualise, predict, test ideas*

This activity provides an opportunity for the children to begin visualising reflections of faces in mirror lines.

Suggested questions:
- Which pictures make a real face?
- Why do you think they will?
- What does a picture need to make a real face?

Jamie's jumper (page 45)
☆ *Processes: look for pattern, predict, test ideas*

The children should make predictions about the colour of Jamie's jumper each time, before they begin colouring and continuing the pattern. Invite the children to create their own jumper puzzles for others to solve.

Suggested questions:
- What colour do you think Jamie's jumper might be?
- Why do you think it will be [red]?

Sorting signs (page 46)
☆ *Processes: reason, explain, co-operate, make decisions*

There are no right or wrong ways of sorting these signs. Some children may collect together signs that look like letters, those that look like numbers or signs, those that are shapes and those that are 'squiggles', whilst others may use other criteria that is personal to them. The importance of this activity is in children being able to explain the features and their reasons for sorting in their particular way. It may be useful to have a spare set of signs for when children become fixed on the idea of a sign being in two sets. This can produce valuable discussions. Ask each pair to explain their sorting to the others in the class, and discuss differences.

Suggested questions:
- Can you explain your groups to us?
- Why did you put this sign in this group?
- Did anyone else sort their signs in this way?
- Grown-ups use this sign when they do maths [×, +, − or =]. Does anyone know what it means?

Lunch boxes (page 47)
☆ *Processes: visualise, reason, record, explain, predict, test ideas*

The children could try a similar activity practically first. They should be encouraged to discuss their ideas with others. It is important that they begin to realise that answers are not always clear-cut and that there is not necessarily a right or wrong answer; it may not be possible to say definitely whether an item will fit into a lunch box.

Suggested questions/prompts:
- Why do you think [a teapot] will not fit in a lunch box?
- Show us how big you think it is with your hands. Does everyone agree?
- Explain to us why you think it might fit.
- Let's look at our different ways of recording.

A classroom hunt (page 48)
☆ *Processes: estimate, record, make decisions, co-operate, compare*

Given the non-exact nature of the terms 'a lot' and 'a few', the children may disagree about certain items. Lead them to appreciate that there are no right or wrong answers, only children's opinions. As a class, try to reach a consensus and generalise about how many we usually mean when we say 'a few' (for example, more than 1 and less than 10).

Suggested questions:
- Which things are there a lot of/a few of?
- How did you record this?
- Did you always agree? Which did you disagree on?
- How many of each thing in the 'a few of' group were there?
- What does this tell us about what we mean by 'a few'?

Pick a pair

- **Work with a friend.**

- **Tick** ✔ **the things which come in** pairs **.**

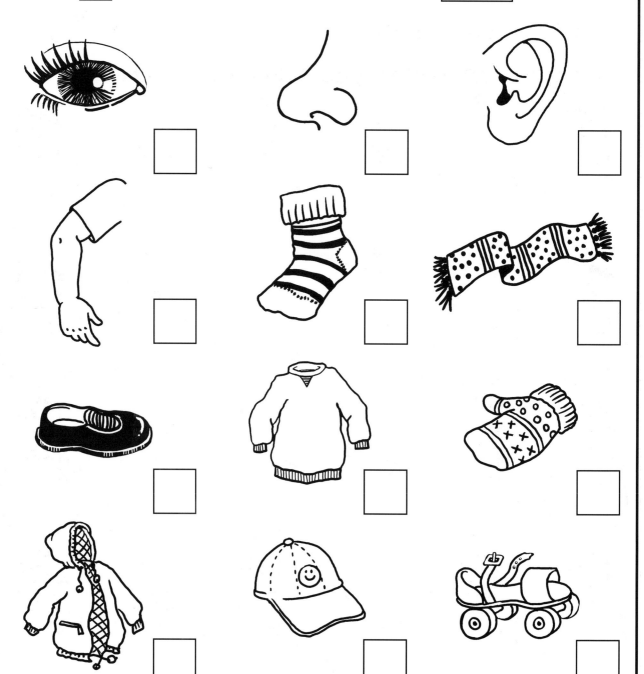

- **Can you think of** 2 **more things that come in pairs? Draw them.**

Teachers' note To encourage further recording work, ask the children to draw two of each of the items they have ticked on plain paper. Display their recordings and use them to reinforce work on counting in twos and early work on even numbers. The children should be encouraged to look out for things that come in twos at home and around the school; these can be drawn and added to the display.

**Developing Numeracy
Using & Applying Maths
Year R
© A & C BLACK**

12

Snowman buttons

Make predictions and test your ideas

- **Use a 1-minute sand timer.**

- **Carefully draw** $\boxed{2}$ **buttons on each snowman.**

- **Ring the snowman you think you will reach.**

- **How many other children finished on the same snowman as you?**

Teachers' note First show the children how to use a one-minute sand timer (or alternatively you could say 'start' and 'stop' after one minute). Ensure the children understand that when the time starts, they are going to draw two buttons on each snowman in turn, working along the rows. Then ask them to predict which snowman they think they will reach in one minute. Discuss and compare their predictions.

Developing Numeracy
Using & Applying Maths
Year R
© A & C BLACK

Record information

- **Listen to the story.**
- **Fill in the** chart .

Time	Animal	Number of pills

Three more animals arrive.

- **Work out the times and the numbers of pills. Show them on the chart.**

Teachers' note Introduce this activity by telling the story suggested on page 7. As the focus is on *beginning* to understand the importance of showing information clearly, it is not reasonable to expect the children to complete the chart accurately. This should be a fun activity which develops naturally from the story. You could ask the children to imagine they are nurses and that they have to remember how many pills to give each animal and at what time.

**Developing Numeracy
Using & Applying Maths
Year R
© A & C BLACK**

14

How many legs?

Record information and make decisions

- **Count how many legs each creature has.**

- **Make a** list **or a** chart **to show this.**

hen

cat

starfish

spider

snake

beetle

snail

crab

Now try this!

- **Draw other creatures.**

- **Show them in your list or chart.**

Teachers' note Give the children plain paper. Encourage them to choose their own method of recording their answers, rather than telling them exactly what to do. Some children may draw the creatures and show the number of legs as a tally, whereas others may use writing and numerals. Once the recordings are made, compare them as a class and discuss decisions that were made: for example, 'Did you decide that a snail has one leg or no legs?'

**Developing Numeracy
Using & Applying Maths
Year R
© A & C BLACK**

All about 3

• **Ring the things that make you think of the number** 3 .

 • **Explain to a friend why you ringed them.**

Teachers' note As the children work, keep reminding them that they should be drawing a ring around the pictures that make them think of the number 3. They might notice features of number, pattern or shape (for example, the 'm' shape looks like a number 3 on its side). Value all suggestions and ensure that the children do not feel that there are 'right answers' to this activity. To reinforce these ideas, a poster could be made of things that remind the class of the number 3.

Developing Numeracy
Using & Applying Maths
Year R
© A & C BLACK

16

Furniture fun

Record information and make decisions

• **Draw or list all the furniture in your classroom.**

• **Tick** ✔ **the correct answer. Are there**

Now try this!

more chairs than tables?   yes ☐   no ☐

more cupboards than tables?   yes ☐   no ☐

Teachers' note Encourage the children to use any form of recording they choose. Some may try pictorial representations; some may use shapes or their own form of tallies; others may draw upon their knowledge of counting and figures when recording. Value all types of recording and ask the children to explain their markings to the class. Compare and discuss them and invite the children to say which type of recording they find easiest to understand. See page 7 for further questions.

Developing Numeracy
Using & Applying Maths
Year R
© A & C BLACK

Toy maze

Look for patterns

- **Follow the paths from** | start | **to** | finish |.

- **Look for patterns.**

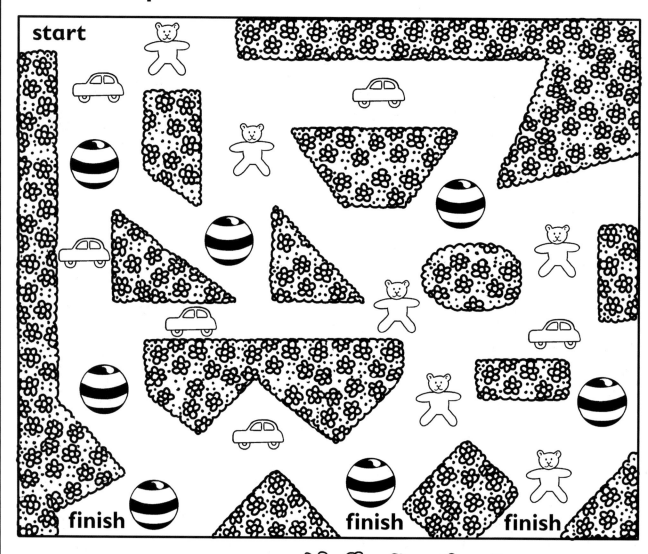

start

finish

finish

finish

- **Draw your patterns.**

_____

_____

_____

Teachers' note Begin by asking the children to find a way from start to finish that goes 'teddy, teddy, teddy, teddy, teddy'. Ask them to look for other ways from start to finish, encouraging them to find any that have patterns (see page 8). Some children may record routes that have no pattern; in such cases, you could draw on a route yourself and ask them to record and explain the pattern. As an extension, the children could draw a maze with toy patterns of their own.

**Developing Numeracy
Using & Applying Maths
Year R
© A & C BLACK**

Fish bowls

- Tick ✔ the bowls that you think have exactly ☐ fish. Do **not** count the fish.

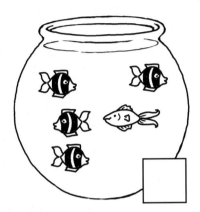

- **Now count the fish. Were you right?**

- **Write how many fish are in each bowl.**

Teachers' note This activity encourages the children to begin seeing sets of objects and gaining a sense of the number of objects without counting each item by pointing to it. Write the number 5 or 6 into the box at the top, according to the abilities of the children. Explain that they must tick the bowls that they *think* have exactly that number of fish. Give the children a limited period of time to do this (for example, 30 seconds), before asking them to check their predictions by counting the fish.

Developing Numeracy
Using & Applying Maths
Year R
© A & C BLACK

19

Duck ponds

Visualise and make predictions

• **Tick** ✔ **the ponds that you think have exactly**

[ ] **ducks. Do not count the ducks.**

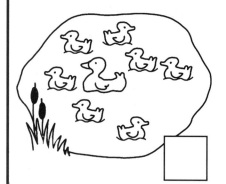 

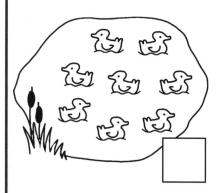 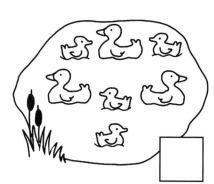 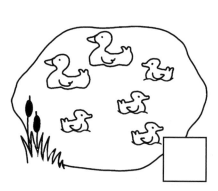

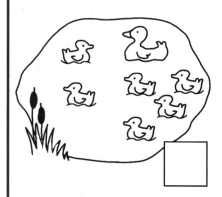  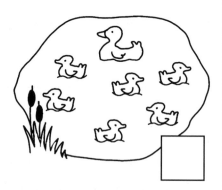

• **Now count the ducks. Were you right?**

 • **Write how many ducks are on each pond.**

Teachers' note This activity encourages the children to begin seeing sets of objects and gaining a sense of the number of objects without counting each item by pointing to it. Write the number 7 or 8 into the box at the top according to the abilities of the children. Explain that they must tick the ponds that they *think* have exactly that number of ducks. Give the children a limited period of time to do this (for example, 30 seconds), before asking them to check their predictions by counting the ducks.

**Developing Numeracy
Using & Applying Maths
Year R
© A & C BLACK**

Letter count

• **How many letters are in your first name?**

• **Count the letters in these names.**

First names of some children in our class

• **Talk to a friend about all the things you notice.**

Now try this! • **Who has the same number of letters in their name as you have?**

Teachers' note Before photocopying, write on the sheet the first names of 18 children in the class, making a note of which names have not been used. At the start of the lesson, display the first names that are not on the sheet and ask the children to identify some of the letters and then to count the letters in the names. Emphasise the importance of checking their counting. Then give the children the activity sheet and ask them to complete it, discussing the things they notice with a partner.

Developing Numeracy
Using & Applying Maths
Year R
© A & C BLACK

Use trial and improvement and be systematic

- **Cut out the squares.**

- **Fit them all together so**

  that [touching] **sides match.**

Make any shape you like.

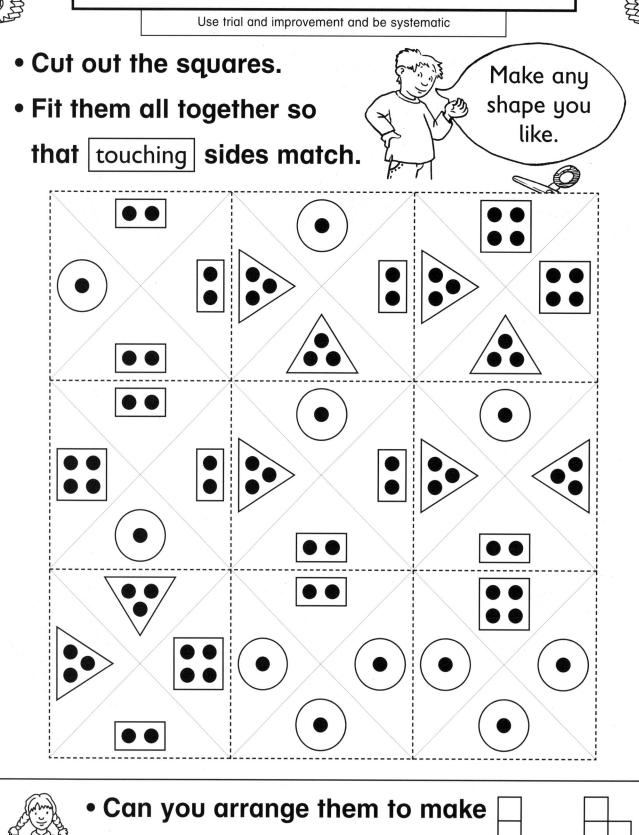

- **Can you arrange them to make**

  these shapes?

Now try this!

Teachers' note The jigsaw pieces could be enlarged onto card and laminated to use as a classroom game. Alternatively, the children can be given a sheet each and asked to cut out their own set of cards. (Remind them to cut along the dotted lines only.) Ask the children to arrange the pieces so that each pair of touching sides has a matching number of dots. For counting practice, the children could count the total number of dots on each piece and record this on the back of the cards.

Developing Numeracy
Using & Applying Maths
Year R
© A & C BLACK

22

In the garden

Visualise

- **Find the numbers hidden in the garden.**

- **Write the numbers.**

 • **Which 2 numbers could this be?**

 or

Teachers' note This visualising activity can develop from work on recognising and writing numerals. At the start of the lesson, encourage the children to draw numerals in the air and to describe the shapes as they draw them: for example, '3 is half round, half round'; '7 is across and down'. Ask the children to watch as you draw a numeral in the air, focusing on whether the sides are curved or straight.

Developing Numeracy
Using & Applying Maths
Year R
© A & C BLACK

23

Asking game

Co-operate and ask your own questions

• **Collect cubes. Ask and answer the questions.**

Teachers' note The children should play this game in small groups, with the help of an adult. They will need a counter each, a dice and some cubes. They should roll the dice, move their counter forward and either collect the number of cubes they land on or ask a question and answer it themselves. Give a cube to children who answer correctly. Where spaces say 'ask', they should think of a question of their own to ask. Discuss suitable questions at the start of the lesson (see page 8).

Developing Numeracy
Using & Applying Maths
Year R
© A & C BLACK

24

Jack's magic beans

Record information

☆ Count some beans into a pot.

☆ Take some out.

☆ How many are left in the pot?

• **Do this** 3 times .

Each time, record what you did.

• **How many beans** altogether **?**

Now try this!

beans

Teachers' note The children should not be told how to record their answers; instead encourage them to choose their own method. Some will draw the beans and use informal symbols to indicate taking away; some might use tallies rather than drawing the beans; others might use figures and standard symbols or words to describe the subtractions. Ask the children to explain their thinking to a partner and to the class.

Developing Numeracy
Using & Applying Maths
Year R
© A & C BLACK

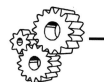

Spacehoppers

Look for patterns and be systematic

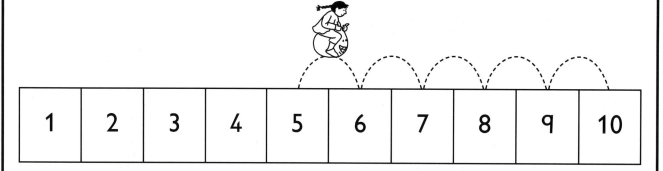

| 1 | 2 | 3 | 4 | 5 | 6 | 7 | 8 | 9 | 10 |

• Write how many hops.

from ☐5 to ☐10   _5_ hops

from ☐2 to ☐5   ____ hops

from ☐1 to ☐6   ____ hops

from ☐2 to ☐8   ____ hops

from ☐7 to ☐10   ____ hops

from ☐5 to ☐6   ____ hop

from ☐6 to ☐8   ____ hops

• Find different ways to make ☐4 hops.

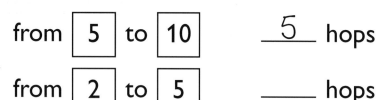

from ☐1 to ☐5   from ☐ to ☐

from ☐ to ☐   from ☐ to ☐

from ☐ to ☐   from ☐ to ☐

Now try this!

Teachers' note The first part of the activity encourages the children to think about the number of hops between two given numbers. Ensure the children understand that they are counting the hops and not the numbers that lie between them.

Developing Numeracy
Using & Applying Maths
Year R
© A & C BLACK

Busy bees

Look for patterns

• **Write how many bees.**

| 3 | add | 1 | is | 4 |

| 1 | add | 3 | is | |

| 2 | add | 4 | is | |

| 4 | add | 2 | is | |

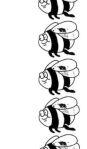

| 1 | add | 5 | is | |

| 5 | add | 1 | is | |

• **Talk to a friend about what you notice.**

 • **Write your own pairs of questions that have the same answer.**

Teachers' note Ensure that the children work across the page, answering each pair of questions, then discussing what they notice with a partner. At the start of the lesson, demonstrate strategies for adding pairs of numbers, such as counting all, counting on, or using a number line. Once the children have noticed a pattern in the numbers, discuss how this can be used to help them answer other questions more quickly: for example, 'If you know 7 + 1, you can find 1 + 7 more quickly.'

Developing Numeracy
Using & Applying Maths
Year R
© A & C BLACK

Kitten on the stairs

Look for patterns and be systematic

The kitten is on a step. It jumps down 2 steps.

• Where does it land?

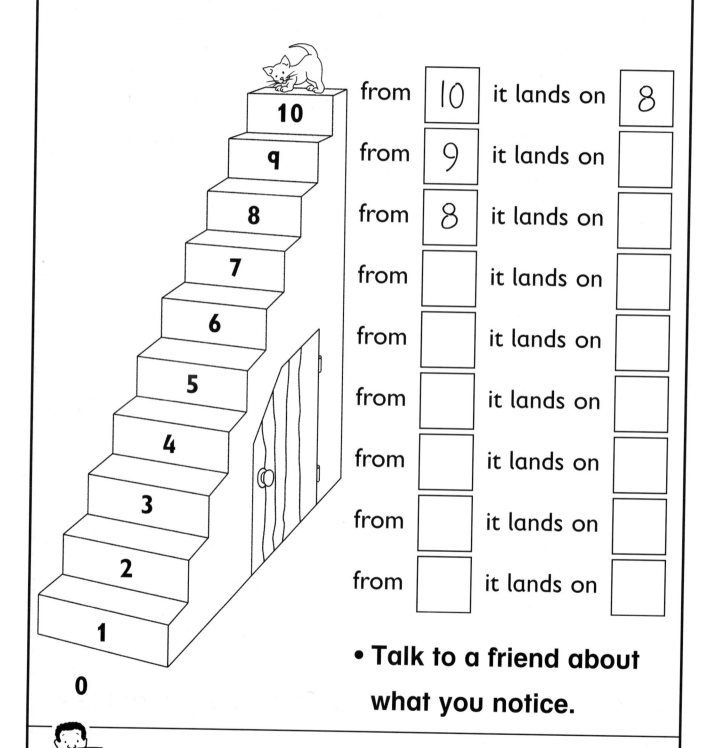

from 10 it lands on 8

from 9 it lands on

from 8 it lands on

from it lands on

from it lands on

from it lands on

from it lands on

from it lands on

from it lands on

• Talk to a friend about what you notice.

Now try this! • **Try this for jumping down 3 steps.**

Teachers' note Encourage the children to describe any patterns they notice in the numbers and to predict what they think the next number will be each time. For the extension activity, the children could record their answers in their own ways or use another version of the sheet. (To adapt the sheet into a flexible resource, mask the worked example and the number 2 at the top so that the sheet can be used to record the results for any number of steps.)

**Developing Numeracy
Using & Applying Maths
Year R
© A & C BLACK**

The dinner queue

Look for patterns

There are ⟦8⟧ children in this queue.

Jo is **third**. | How many in front? | 2
How many behind? | ___

Ann is **fifth**. | How many in front? |
How many behind? | ___

Dev is **fourth**. | How many in front? |
How many behind? | ___

Tom is **second**. | How many in front? |
How many behind? | ___

Kim is **seventh**. | How many in front? |
How many behind? | ___

• **Add each pair of numbers. What do you notice?**

Now try this!

• **What if there were ⟦6⟧ children in the queue?**

Teachers' note Demonstrate this activity practically before the children work on the activity sheet. The activity revises ordinal numbers, but its main emphasis is on looking for patterns in the answers and explaining observations. For a queue of 8 children, all pairs of numbers should add to 7, similarly for a queue of 6 the numbers will add to 5. Encourage the children to ask their own questions and to explore other queues in this way.

**Developing Numeracy
Using & Applying Maths
Year R
© A & C BLACK**

Make decisions and record information

- **Look at the menu on *At the café: 2*.**

- **Choose a** `main dish` **and a** `dessert`.

- **Work out the total** `cost`.

  cost £ _____

  cost £ _____

  cost £ _____

- **Talk to a friend about your meals.**

- **Which was** `cheapest` **?**

- **Which was** `most expensive` **?**

Teachers' note The children will need a copy of the menu on page 31. Encourage them to record their choices of main dish and dessert in their own way: for example, by drawing the choices, writing only the prices or even using words or letters. When the children are discussing their meals, encourage them to ask and answer their own questions: for example, 'What would be the most expensive/cheapest meal I could have? How many different meals could I have that cost exactly £5?'

Developing Numeracy
Using & Applying Maths
Year R
© A & C BLACK

Make decisions and record information

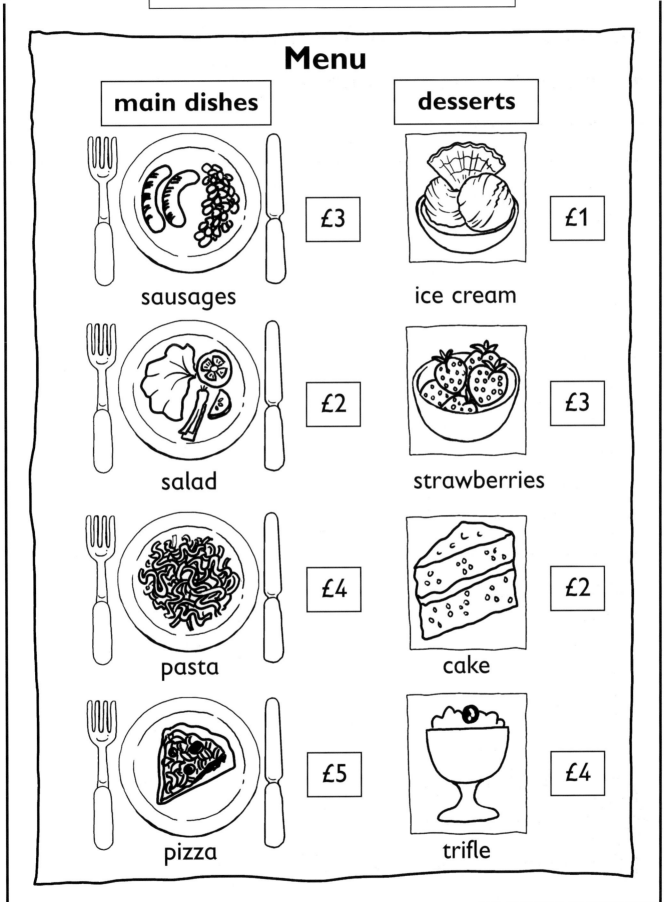

Menu

main dishes

sausages — £3

salad — £2

pasta — £4

pizza — £5

desserts

ice cream — £1

strawberries — £3

cake — £2

trifle — £4

Teachers' note This sheet should be used with the activity on page 30. It could be copied onto card and laminated for further use in informal play and role play in the play area.

Developing Numeracy
Using & Applying Maths
Year R
© A & C BLACK

Peas in a pod

Look for patterns and be systematic

Sam has some peas in each hand.

• How many peas has he | altogether | **?**

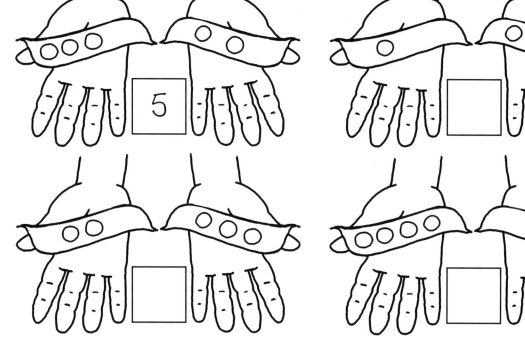

• Talk to a friend about what you notice.

• Draw ways of making 6 **peas altogether.**

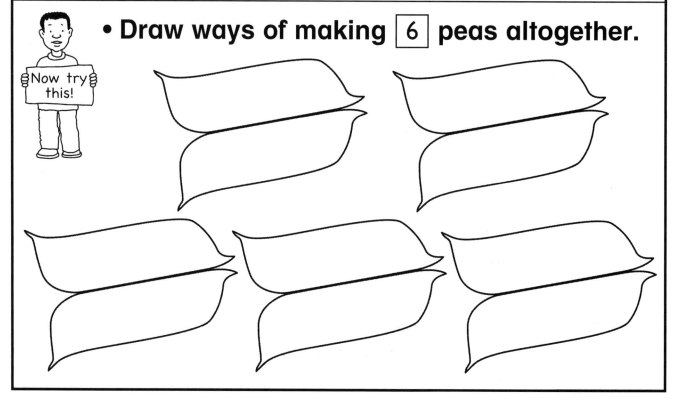

Now try this!

Teachers' note The children could go on to investigate ways of making 7, 8, 9 or 10 peas altogether. Encourage them to work systematically (see page 9). A display or poster could be made to show all the ways; each day, remove one and ask the children to say which is missing. Children doing the extension activity could use counters to help them.

Developing Numeracy
Using & Applying Maths
Year R
© A & C BLACK

Make predictions

- **Tick ✔ the trays that you <u>think</u> have an answer that is** `more than 6` **.**

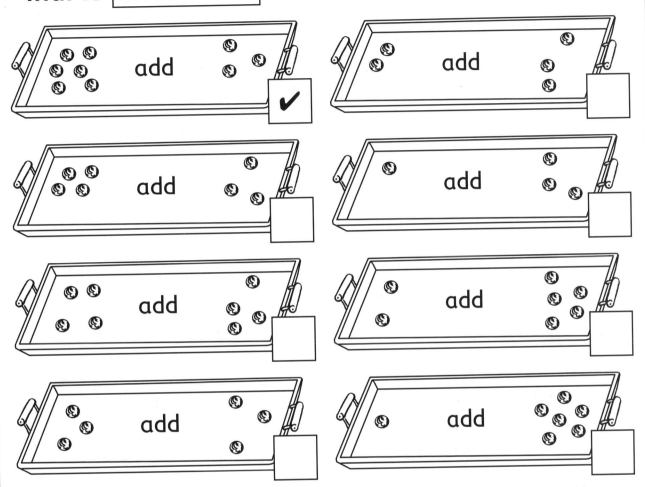

- **Now add the marbles. Were you right?**

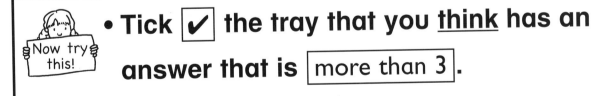

- **Tick ✔ the tray that you <u>think</u> has an answer that is** `more than 3` **.**

Now try this!

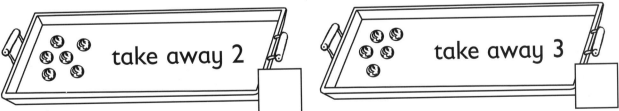

- **Now find the answers to check.**

Teachers' note Ensure the children realise that they should predict which answers will be greater than 6 *without* working out the answers first. Once they have ticked the boxes, they should work out the answers to check their predictions. Some of the marbles could be masked before photocopying and the children asked to predict which trays have an answer of more than 4 or 5, depending on ability.

**Developing Numeracy
Using & Applying Maths
Year R
© A & C BLACK**

Biscuit take away

Look for patterns

- **Cross off** $\boxed{2}$ **biscuits.**

- **How many biscuits are left on the plate?**

| $\boxed{3}$ take away 2 is $\boxed{1}$ | $\boxed{4}$ take away 2 is $\boxed{}$ |

| $\boxed{5}$ take away 2 is $\boxed{}$ | $\boxed{6}$ take away 2 is $\boxed{}$ |

| $\boxed{7}$ take away 2 is $\boxed{}$ | $\boxed{8}$ take away 2 is $\boxed{}$ |

Now try this!

- **Draw your own biscuit take away.**

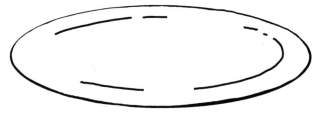

$\boxed{}$ take away $\boxed{}$ is $\boxed{}$

Teachers' note Once the activity sheet has been completed, ask the children to read the questions and answers aloud to reinforce the sounds of the patterns. Ask them to use this pattern to predict answers to other questions, such as 9 take away 2 or 10 take away 2. The children could investigate taking away 3 or 4 from numbers up to 10 and record and describe the patterns they notice.

Developing Numeracy
Using & Applying Maths
Year R
© A & C BLACK

Crazy caterpillars

Look for patterns and co-operate

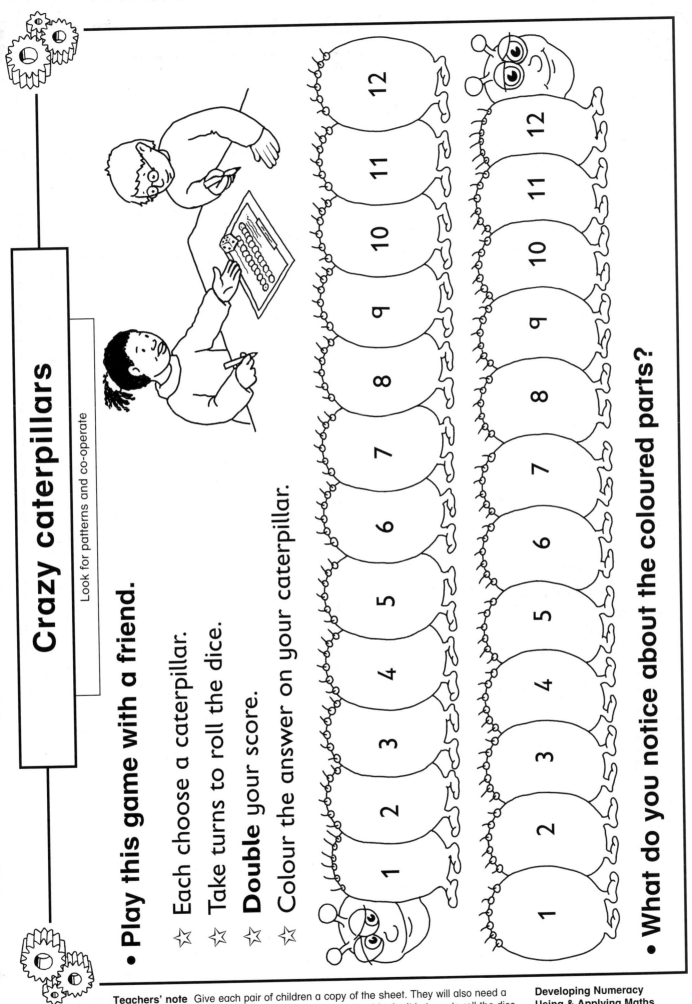

- **Play this game with a friend.**

☆ Each choose a caterpillar.

☆ Take turns to roll the dice.

☆ **Double** your score.

☆ Colour the answer on your caterpillar.

| 1 | 2 | 3 | 4 | 5 | 6 | 7 | 8 | 9 | 10 | 11 | 12 |

| 1 | 2 | 3 | 4 | 5 | 6 | 7 | 8 | 9 | 10 | 11 | 12 |

- **What do you notice about the coloured parts?**

Developing Numeracy
Using & Applying Maths
Year R
© A & C BLACK

Teachers' note Give each pair of children a copy of the sheet. They will also need a coloured pencil each and a spot dice. The children should take it in turns to roll the dice, double their score and colour that number on their caterpillar, continuing until they cannot colour in any more numbers. Encourage them to notice that only every other number, i.e. the even numbers, can be coloured.

Swirling spirals

Make predictions and test your ideas

• **Tick** ✔ **the letter that you <u>think</u> will make**

the longest spiral   **the shortest** spiral

A ☐   B ☐   C ☐   A ☐   B ☐   C ☐

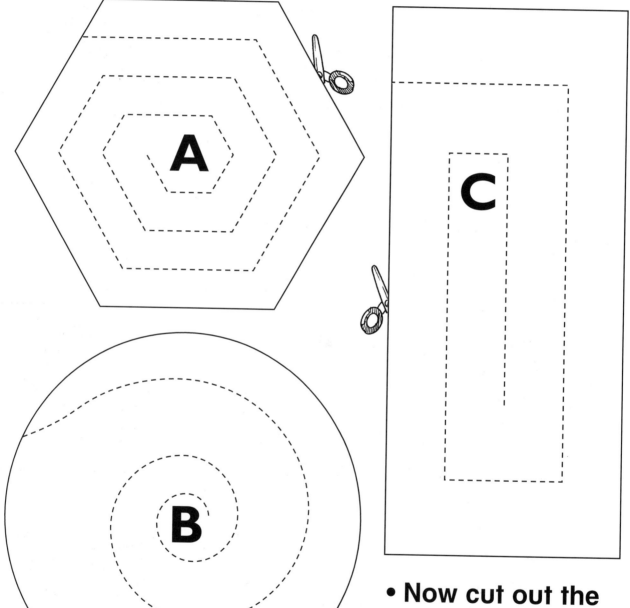

A

C

B

• **Now cut out the shapes and make the spirals.**

Teachers' note Begin the lesson by demonstrating how to make a hanging spiral, starting from a simple shape and cutting around in a spiral. Show the children the shapes on the activity sheet and ask them to predict which will make the longest and shortest spirals. (The length of a spiral is how far down it falls.) A class record could be made of the number of children who predict A, B or C in each case. Then ask the children to test their ideas by cutting out the shapes and making the spirals.

Developing Numeracy
Using & Applying Maths
Year R
© A & C BLACK

Roll and slide

Make predictions, visualise and test your ideas

- ## Work with a friend.

- ## Which things do you __think__ will

| roll | **or** | slide | **or** | roll **and** slide | ?

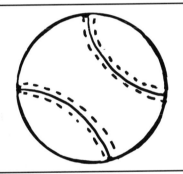

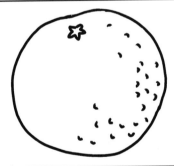

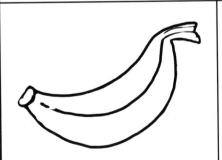

- ## Now test the things. Were you right?

Teachers' note First tell the children that they are going to push each of these items down a slope, and their task is to decide which items will roll, which will slide and which might do both. The children can be encouraged to record their predictions in a number of ways (see page 10). You will need the objects shown on this sheet (or similar objects) and a sloping surface for the children to test their predictions. This can be done either in small groups or as a class.

Developing Numeracy
Using & Applying Maths
Year R
© A & C BLACK

37

Paperclip pythons

Make predictions and test your ideas

• **Guess how many paperclips can be fitted together to match the length of each snake.**

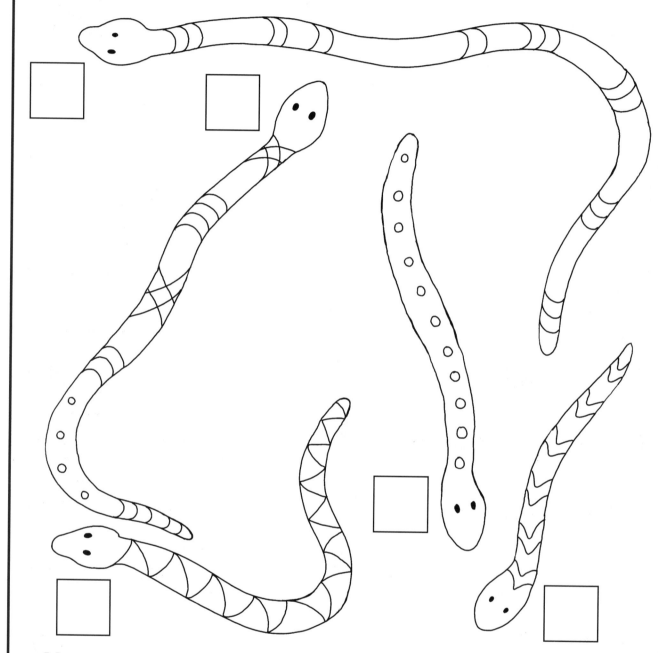

• **Now use paperclips to test your guesses.**

Now try this!

• **Draw a snake about ⬚7 paperclips long.**
• **Check your drawing.**

Teachers' note Before beginning, show the children how paperclips can be linked together. Ask the children to write their guesses in the boxes on the sheet. Invite them to talk to others about their predictions and encourage discussion about why they chose the numbers they did: for example, 'This snake looks longer than this one, so I put a bigger number.' Then provide each child with about ten paperclips, and ask them to test their guesses.

**Developing Numeracy
Using & Applying Maths
Year R
© A & C BLACK**

Who can see who?

Visualise

• **Put cubes on the grey boxes to make walls.**

Can the 🕷 see the 🐭 ?	✔ yes	☐ no
Can the 🐭 see the 🐸 ?	☐ yes	☐ no
Can the 🐛 see the 🐞 ?	☐ yes	☐ no
Can the 🐞 see the 🐸 ?	☐ yes	☐ no
Can the 🐛 see the 🕷 ?	☐ yes	☐ no

• **Talk about this question with a friend.**

Now try this!

Who can the see?

Teachers' note Visualising a situation from another point of view is a skill that children find very difficult. Ask them to imagine that they are one of the creatures on the map and tell them that the cubes are tall walls. Could they see each of the other creatures? The children could also make their own 'maps' using small toys and cubes for walls, and try a similar activity.

**Developing Numeracy
Using & Applying Maths
Year R
© A & C BLACK**

Teddy boys

Be systematic

Teddy is wearing a T-shirt, shorts and a hat.

- Use red , blue and yellow pencils.

- Colour Teddy's outfit. Make it different each time.

Teachers' note Explain that in an outfit, the clothes do not have to be all different colours; they can be all the same, two the same, or all different. Once the children have completed the sheet, they should cut out the teddies and, with a partner, sort their cards in different ways: for example, all the teddies with a blue hat, all those with red shorts, and so on. They could be given an extra sheet to colour more outfits if they think of other colour combinations.

Developing Numeracy
Using & Applying Maths
Year R
© A & C BLACK

Stepping out

Make estimates and record information

You need chicken steps and duck steps .

- Estimate how many steps.

  Write in pencil.

- Then check. Write in pen.

across your table	along a ruler
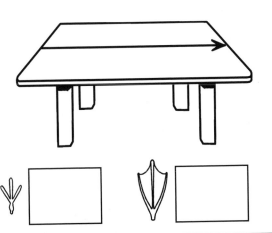	
along your tray	along a piece of paper
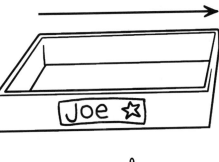 	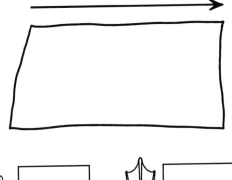 

- **Estimate steps for other things in the classroom. Then check.**

Teachers' note The children will need copies of the cards on pages 42 and 43. Show them the chicken steps and duck steps and explain that they should estimate and write in pencil the number of steps (placed 'heel to toe') across the items in the classroom shown on the sheet. They should then use the cards to check, and ink in the actual number.

Developing Numeracy
Using & Applying Maths
Year R
© A & C BLACK

Make estimates and record information

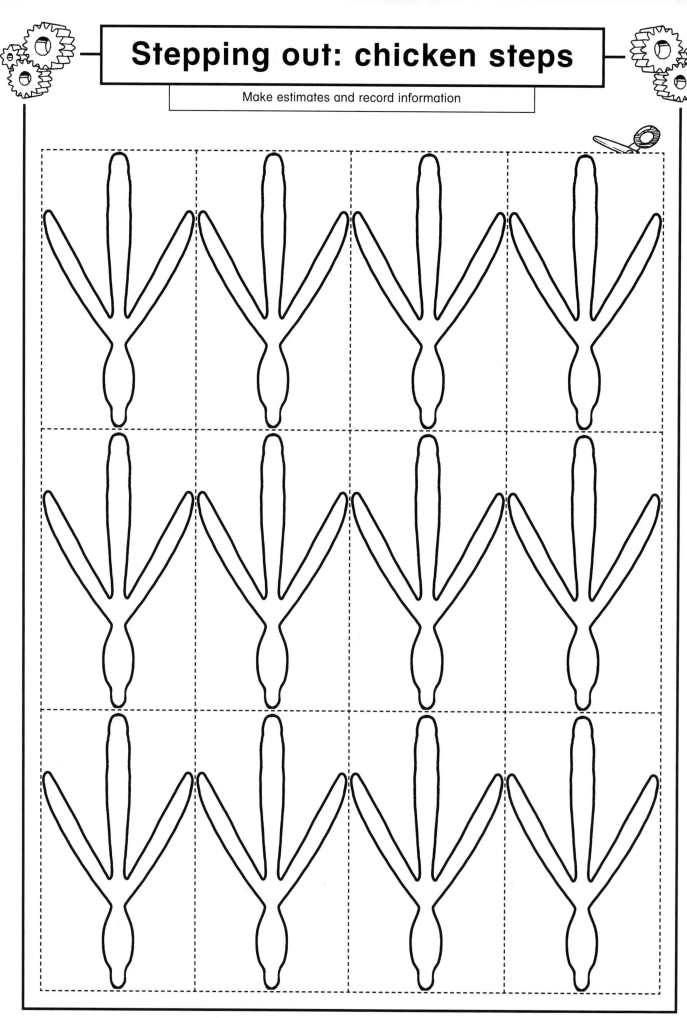

Teachers' note These cards should be cut out and used in conjunction with pages 41 and 43. (See also the activity notes on page 11.) The cards could be laminated to create a more permanent resource.

Developing Numeracy
Using & Applying Maths
Year R
© A & C BLACK

Make estimates and record information

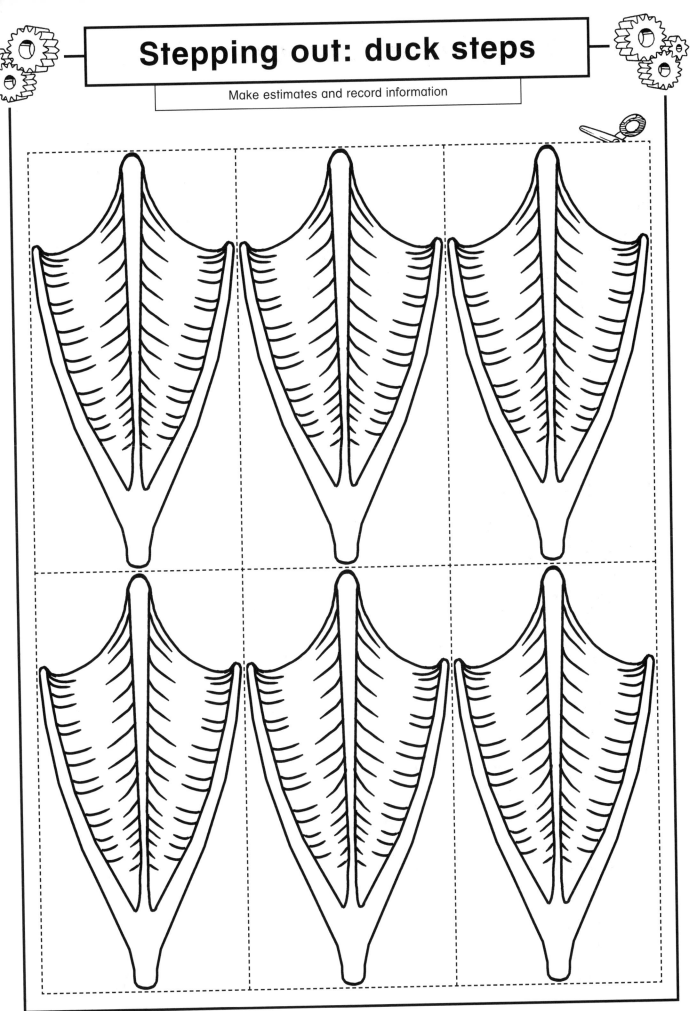

Teachers' note These cards should be cut out and used in conjunction with pages 41 and 42. (See also the activity notes on page 11.) The cards could be laminated to create a more permanent resource.

Developing Numeracy
Using & Applying Maths
Year R
© A & C BLACK

Smiley faces

• **Tick** ✔ **the half faces that you <u>think</u> will make real faces when a mirror is placed on the line.**

• **Talk to a friend about your choices.**

• **Now use a mirror to check.**

Now try this!

• **Draw a half face of your own that works.**

• **Now draw a half face that does <u>not</u> work.**

Teachers' note Once the children have predicted and discussed which will make real faces, give them mirrors so that they can check. The children could be asked to draw the reflections of the real faces on the sheet. For further practice in visualising, the faces on this sheet could be masked and redrawn so that the children have a greater number to predict.

**Developing Numeracy
Using & Applying Maths
Year R**
© A & C BLACK

Jamie's jumper

Look for patterns

These jumpers are in a pattern.

- **Guess the colour of Jamie's jumper.** • **Colour to check.**

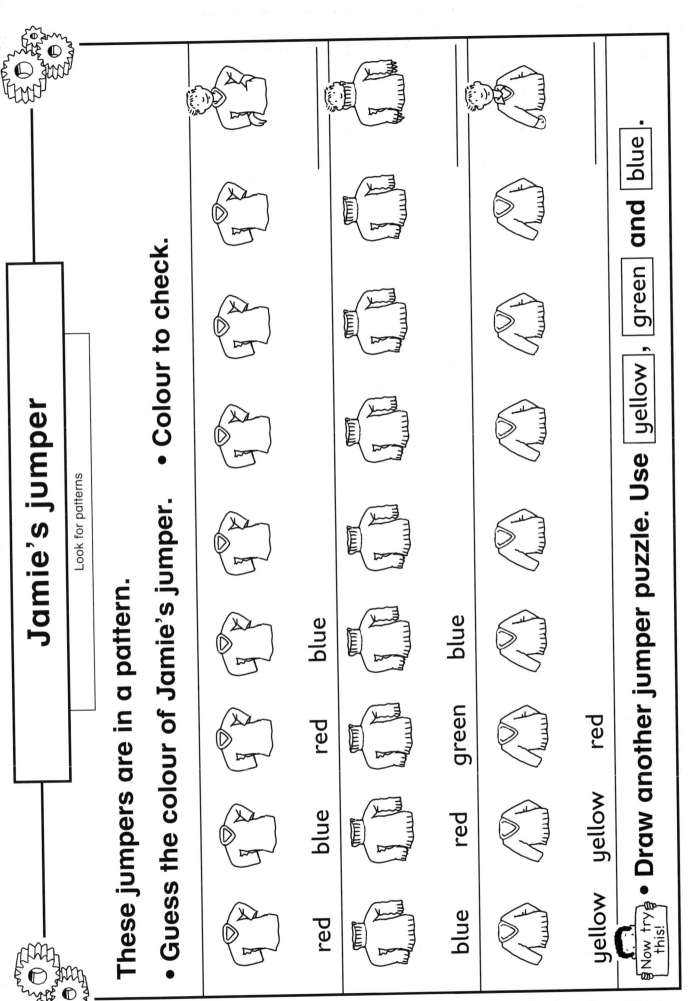

red   blue   red   blue

blue   red   green   blue

yellow   yellow   red

- **Draw another jumper puzzle. Use** yellow , green **and** blue .

Now try this!

Teachers' note Read the names of the colours with the children and provide a word
bank of the names written in the appropriate colour.

**Developing Numeracy
Using & Applying Maths
Year R
© A & C BLACK**

45

Sorting signs

- ## Cut out the cards.

- ## With a friend, sort the signs into groups.

Teachers' note This sheet could be enlarged onto A3. Provide one sheet per pair. Encourage the children to talk to each other about the signs and to decide how they would like to sort them. Accept any ways of sorting, encouraging the children to explain their reasoning to others. The cards could be stuck onto sheets of paper in their sets. See also the activity notes on page 11.

Developing Numeracy
Using & Applying Maths
Year R
© A & C BLACK

- **Will a football fit in a lunch box?**

- **Draw things that you think <u>will</u> fit in a lunch box.**

- **Draw things that you think <u>will not</u> fit.**

- **Ring the things that you think <u>will</u> fit.**

Now try this!

Teachers' note First discuss what 'fit in' might mean: for example, a football might sit inside a lunch box, but the lid probably would not close. Establish what the children think 'fit in' should mean. Initially, this activity should be done without testing to encourage the children to make predictions and visualise. The children should be given the opportunity to explain their reasoning and, where possible, to test their predictions. See also page 11.

Developing Numeracy
Using & Applying Maths
Year R
© A & C BLACK

A classroom hunt

- ## Work with a friend.

- ## Look around your classroom.

- ## Collect information about things that there are:

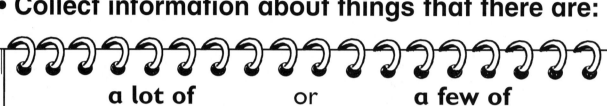

a lot of   or   **a few of**

Now try this!

- ## Look at the things that there are a few of .

- ## Count how many of each thing there are.

Teachers' note This activity encourages pairs of children to co-operate in finding things around the classroom that there are a lot of or a few of. Invite the children to suggest how many might be 'a lot' and how many might be 'a few'. Rather than telling the children exactly how to record their answers, encourage them to choose their own way to show the information. Some children may draw pictures whilst others may use writing.

Developing Numeracy
Using & Applying Maths
Year R
© A & C BLACK